FIRST STORY
CHANGING LIVES THROUGH WRITING

There is dignity and power in telling our own story. We help young people find their voices.

First Story places professional writers into secondary schools serving low-income communities, where they work intensively with students and teachers to foster confidence, creativity and writing ability.

Our programmes expand young people's horizons and raise aspirations. Students gain vital skills that underpin their success in school and support their transition to further education and employment.

To find out more and get involved, go to
www.firststory.org.uk.

First Story is a registered charity number 1122939 and a private company limited by guarantee incorporated in England with number 06487410. First Story is a business name of First Story Limited.

First published 2021 by First Story Limited
44 Webber Street, Southbank, London, SE1 8QW

www.firststory.org.uk

ISBN 978-0-85748-498-7

1 3 5 7 9 10 8 6 4 2

A CIP catalogue record for this book is available from the British Library.

Printed and bound in the UK by Aquatint
Typeset by Avon DataSet Ltd
Copyedited by Sally Beets
Proofread by Sophie Blacksell Jones
Cover illustration by The Man Trout

A Written Masquerade

An Anthology by the First Story Group
at Dukeries Academy

Edited by Kevin Fegan | 2021

FIRST STORY
CHANGING LIVES THROUGH WRITING

As Patron of First Story I am delighted that it continues to foster and inspire the creativity and talent of young people in secondary schools serving low-income communities.

I firmly believe that nurturing a passion for reading and writing is vital to the health of our country. I am therefore greatly encouraged to know that young people in this school — and across the country — have been meeting each week throughout the year in order to write together.

I send my warmest congratulations to everybody who is published in this anthology.

Camilla

HRH The Duchess of Cornwall

Contents

Introduction

Kevin Fegan, Writer-in-Residence

It has been a real pleasure to work with this intriguing group of Year 12 students. They are an imaginative and refreshingly mature group of young people. In addition to writing poetry and prose, I also invited the students to explore playwriting. Obviously, plays are studied in English Literature; but not often in creative writing. The examples selected are students' first attempts at writing the opening of a new play and should be read as such.

Previously, I had worked with Tanya Russell in another school as First Story Writer-in-Residence; so, when Tanya invited me to work with her at Dukeries Academy, I was thrilled. Tanya is an inspirational teacher. However, there is an underlying sadness to this residency. I was moved to tears when this group of Year 12 students asked if they could dedicate their anthology to the memory of their beloved Physics teacher, Mrs Emma Fegan. I knew that Emma's husband (and my nephew), Richard, was deeply touched by the genuine sense of loss expressed by students and staff at Dukeries, following the tragic death of his wife. Richard has given us permission to include the dedication.

Teacher's Foreword

Tanya Russell, Lead Practitioner – Senior Leadership Team

Introducing First Story to our students was really exciting because, having participated in First Story projects before with the fantastic Kevin Fegan, I knew that they were embarking on a journey to discover their inner writers and hopefully to learn more about themselves. It was even more important to me because this collection was going to be written by students from The Dukeries Academy, the school that I attended as a child, the place where I first discovered my own writing voice.

I also knew that the students participating in the project were inspiring young people who, during what has undeniably been a very difficult year, would still allow their bravery, resilience and intelligence to shine through. My students are thoughtful, tolerant individuals who indicate why First Story is such an important project. These students have voices that should be listened to and working with an experienced writer has really helped them to hone their skill so that their ideas are translated into the best possible words to express their wonder and worries as they look at the world changing around them.

I am incredibly proud of this collection because it represents a community that is integral to my own identity. These young writers have expressed their inner selves brilliantly and contemplated the strange times that we have all experienced in a year that left us often alone with our thoughts. That my students have managed to harness those thoughts and turn them into something positive, full of hope while acknowledging that pain, makes this anthology something really special.

This anthology is dedicated to the memory of our Physics Teacher, Mrs Emma Fegan

When You Were My Teacher

Laura Richardson

Physics – a subject that most
don't understand
I wish I could still have your guidance
as if you were holding my hand
because when you were my teacher
you helped me to comprehend
what 'Newton's Second Law' is
and if friction works on sand

when you were my teacher in Year 8
you brought me up in front of the class
to tell them about my future
and when I told you I was shy
you said to focus on the bigger picture
so I did as I was told
and talked about our ever-growing culture
of finding out where we come from
and every living creature

when you were my teacher in Year 9
I didn't like Physics much
I didn't understand 'spring constant'
and other things such
as 'half-lives'
now I wish to clutch
my level up again
hoping to have
the magic touch
you gave long ago

so, when you were my teacher
you gave me a golden tie
you stood upon the stage
and told a speech about why
I won the 'Biology Award' and
how much I have come out of my shy
shell for when you were my teacher
time would fly by
and now I wish I could go back all those years
and understand why
I didn't appreciate you more

because when you were my teacher, I...

Are We There Yet?

Abigail Horne

so here i am now,
i find myself drifting through the darkness,
being swallowed into the unknown abyss.
i am scared. i am apprehensive.
do you understand emotions?
feelings?
connections?

if you find this, please understand my message,
listen. consider it. listen again.

are you there?
do you understand me?
my language?
my speech?
my words?
any signal will do –
let me know you are there.

are we there yet?
i come from a small planet named earth.
beautiful. perfect. pure.
where the sky is blue
and the sun shines.
can you see the sun?
a giant ball of hydrogen,
the star we rely on,
our star.

are we there yet?
i am on my own mission
to find you,
'discover a new life',
we're all waiting for you.
i think I'm getting closer,
the signal is growing stronger.

are we there yet?
please respond, we need answers.
do you have answers?
maybe you have the answer:
is there life on mars?

so, i'll ask again,
are we there yet?

My Clean Ocean Dreams

Abigail Horne

Performing tricks in my small pool, instead of in the sea,
I don't care about the claps and kisses,
I'd rather be free, in the blue sky above me;
It reminds me of home.

You force me to do dance, but I don't want to,
I'd prefer to breach into the horizon.
Little girls smile when I whistle
And ask their mummies if they can 'buy one?'

They cheer because we've been 'saved'
From the plastic sea monsters,
Yet they are blind to realise
They're the ones who contaminated my waters.

So, help me: swap your plastic straws for metal
And don't throw your rubbish into the sea.
Check if your package is biodegradable
And please consider me

And my clean ocean dreams.

Realisation

Alisha Knowles

Scene One

Present day. Liam is an early twenties male with recently dyed, light pink hair that is pulled up in a half bun. He has an athletic physique and stands at 6'3". Liam is standing on his porch, looking out to his farm, with a bottle of gin open in his hand and a sack of collected potatoes next to him.

Liam: *(Smashing the bottle on the ground next to him)* God! Why, why do I keep getting this reoccurring thought? I do not need to constantly be reminded of what I did wrong.

(To the audience) Life is a funny thing. Move too fast and you get put down; move too slow, you get put down. No matter what, you always get put down. I'm sick of it. You fight for a country that you're supposed to feel proud of, but all I am is left with regret.

(Kicking the bag of potatoes) He should not have been shot. It should have been me. He did not deserve this. Sure, he might have been like Icarus and flown too close to the sun, but he had a future, unlike me.

He slumps to the ground, pulls the tags out of his pocket and clutches them to his chest.

I am done. I am done with it all. Why should I fight for a country that does not care for the fallen? He died for this country, and what did his family get in return? A thanks for his service. A measly thanks. What will that accomplish? That will not help fix the trauma they will have to live through. It won't help fix what I have seen.

It will not fix the guilt I have. Violence is no longer the way forward for me.

(*Putting the tag on his chain*) I regret all that I have done. I do not want to go back. I am sick of this system of reoccurring violence. I want to be safe. I want to be free. I want to protect my last remaining friend. All I want is peace.

He kneels down and puts the potatoes back in the bag. He stands up and opens the door to his small cottage. He turns around, gives everything a once over and walks into his house.

Scene Two

Liam is in a meadow in the forest behind his farm, dressed in a formal, white, buttoned-up shirt and black skinny jeans, his hair pulled into a plait. He has just returned from his friend's funeral. He has an old book with him, The Art of War.

Liam: This is beautiful. I'm so glad that I managed to buy the farm. I needed a change of scenery; I needed this tranquillity. I needed it after that dreadful silence of the funeral; I don't think I can go through that again.

Sitting down under the largest tree, he re-reads the book. He doesn't see Phil approach. Phil has shaggy blonde hair and is wearing a green T-shirt and black jeans and a white and green hat. He is around 5'7". He sneaks up behind Liam to scare him.

Phil: Oi!

Liam throws the book, swings around and accidently right-hooks Phil, knocking him to the ground.

Liam   What the hell was that for?

Phil: (*Rubbing his jaw in pain*) I dunno, I just felt like it. It was a brilliant opportunity.

Liam pulls the older man up and they share a brief hug.

Phil: So, how have you been? It feels like we haven't talked in years! I know that can't be helped, but now that you're back we can spend so much more time together. It's been lonely without you here. I've missed you so much.

Liam: Slow down, I'm not going anywhere. For what it's worth, I missed you too.

Phil: This place hasn't been the same without you here; it's been too quiet. I always enjoyed coming down to help you fix the problems you caused.

They laugh.

Liam: Yeah, you totally enjoyed being woken up at midnight cause all my pigs managed to escape and spending six hours looking for them.

Phil: Hey, I wouldn't have done that if I didn't care about you.

Liam: Come on, Phil, it's getting cold; we don't want to freeze out here. I miss those times, free from the constant fighting. God, I'm glad to be home.

Phil: I bet you are. Now you have more time to read; I'm actually surprised that you haven't wrote a book yet with how much time you have on your hands.

Liam: Like I could write a book. I'm not *that* bored.

Phil: I wouldn't put it past you.

Scene Three

Inside the cottage.

Phil: Now tell me how you really feel, mate.

Liam Really? I'm doing just fantastic! I spend all day farming and, in the evenings, I try to read. But, y'know, that doesn't always happen. I'm constantly haunted by the screams and the whistle of bullets. I hear Will's cries as he bleeds out while I just stand there; I can't do anything. Other than that, though, I am doing just amazing.

Phil: (*To audience*) Y'know, I'm surprised he didn't break down earlier, but then again Liam isn't one to break down in front of people. He cares far too much about how others are and what they will think of him, neglecting himself constantly. It's a vicious cycle and he's feeding into it, day after day. He needs help, but he will not come to me. I've been his friend for many years, all the way back to our childhood, yet he still won't open up fully. I care deeply about him. I can't let him continuously slip into the cycle. I can't watch him being chipped away, fractured, any longer.

Reliving the Past

Alisha Knowles

Sat, looking around the boring, plain, lilac room, I thought about the past and how free I was and how packed the latter half of the year was. Grabbing my phone, I saw a new suggestion: 'Relive the Past'. With curiosity, I downloaded the app, unaware of what was about to happen.

It seemed like hours had passed until my phone dinged. The app had finally downloaded. I had no idea what it was, realising how stupid and lazy it was to download a random, suggested app. I contemplated whether it was worth it. Too curious to turn back, I continued forward and launched the app. A burst of vibrant yellows, oranges and crimsons filled the screen, surrounding the words 'Relive the Past.' Fully intrigued, I pressed continue and went further down this rabbit hole of mixed emotions. It asked me to type the name of a past loved one. Confused, I typed in the name of my best friend, my grandad, who I did not get to see before he passed. Pressing OK, I looked out of the window, the sun was setting, creating wisps of orange and baby pink, embracing the blues and purples taking over.

It must not have taken more than five minutes before a flash of cyan filled the room and, the next thing I knew, my grandad was perched on the end of my bed. Full of disbelief, I instantly reached forward for his hand and was shocked that my hand did not pass through his – it rested on top. In a sudden burst, all my old memories with him came rushing back and I could not help but smile. This was a chance to say everything I did not manage to that night; this was my chance to re-live the events from when I was younger, a chance to get to know him more than I already did. Staring straight at me, the kind, lanky man smiled the same smile he had when my family and I appeared at his bungalow. He always embraced the socialisation and care we brought with us. Eventually, he moved back into our home, his old house, where he could not escape the constant flow of conversation and jokes between everyone in the last years of his life. The laughs forever embedded in the walls, combatting the sadness and emptiness I felt whenever I walk into what used to be his room. The gentle giant had not changed since I last saw him. The white hair was curled in the exact same place; he was still the same height, and he was wearing his favourite outfit: blue jeans and a blue polo shirt with a cyan sweater. I looked into his eyes, those clear, soft, baby-blue eyes that were always filled with kindness – a kindness near impossible to find nowadays. Memories came rushing back: walking in the forest, picking mushrooms, watching the 'Robin Hood Festival', going to his bungalow every Saturday to stay the night, watching *Strictly Come Dancing* and then the Lotto numbers being read out. He smiled, causing the flood of tears I was holding back to be released. Rushing towards him, I embraced him in the same familiar hold. Trembling and stammering, managed to spit out an apology for not being there the night he left, for not holding his hand. He shook his head and held me tightly, reassuring me that it was okay, that he didn't want me to see him in pain. We sat near each other, him in his old trusty chair that I was fortunately allowed to keep. We just talked and talked about his life up to the year he passed. He told stories of what he saw. Time seemed to fly by, the hours slowly creeping away and it came to the time he had to leave. I embraced him for the last time, like I should have on the day he left and whispered goodbye. He uttered the words, 'It'll be okay, we'll see each other soon.' He grew more transparent until I was left alone, tears rolling unknowingly down my face.

I lay on my bed, curled up with the cuddly toy he bought me – a gorilla. Hiding my face in the gorilla, I remembered the last couple of hours, contentment slowly filling me.

Time Travel

Annie Lewis

The advertisement read: 'New VR app and goggles to match!
Let's you travel to the era of your choosing!' The man squinted
up at the violently neon sign; it glared down at him, coaxing
him in to make the purchase. A sudden realisation that his
birthday was only a couple of days away made him shrug his
shoulders and enter the shop. A store clerk, a smile plastered
permanently on her face, guided him towards a pedestal
where stood the highly anticipated technological advancement
of the century. He left the store with an unfamiliar feeling of
excitement.

Returning home, the man carried his new possession into
his living room. He pulled the goggles out of the box and held
them up to the light. The back of the packaging instructed him
to download an app entitled 'era expedition', connect the
goggles and scan a relic to travel to the time period when it was
made. Unable to wait another minute, he drove to the museum
where he worked his nine-to-five. Upon arrival, he turned his
half-rusted key in the door and opened it into a darkened room
with a sky-high ceiling. His leather shoes skidded on the
marble floor, almost tripping him up. He placed his phone to
face a glass case containing the broken fragments of an
Ancient Greek pottery vase. The phone screen was illuminated
by the magnificent piece of history, which was restored to its
full, original glory. After gazing admiringly at the screen for
a few moments, the man removed the VR goggles from his
bag and covered his eyes with them. He hesitated slightly
before pressing his finger on the large green button covered
by the word 'travel' in bold letters. His arm shot up to shield

his eyes from the scorching sun as he attempted to adjust to his surroundings: Ancient Athens. The city was bustling with civilians draped in white fabric and with horse-drawn chariots – one of which almost knocked the man off his feet. In need of a rest from this dramatically different way of life, he reached up to his eyes to remove the goggles he had put on just two minutes earlier, only to realise there was nothing there to take off. Panicked, the man clawed around at his head in desperation but realised there was little hope. He sighed and collapsed onto a large, uneven rock to gather his thoughts. As the stages of grief set in, it dawned on him that he would need to find some way to survive in this uncertain and unknown world.

Eleanor

Annie Lewis

Back Story

This is the beginning of a play about a 16-year-old girl, by the name of Eleanor Goldsmith, who lives in East Anglia during the time of Matthew Hopkins' infamous witch hunts (1645–47). Eleanor's parents are respected in the town. She is of outstanding intelligence and is especially interested in Astronomy and Physics but has to hide her genius from everyone, including her parents. She has learned to read by working for a merchant who gives her spare books. She disguises herself as a boy, but the merchant is aware of her true identity; he supports her passion. However, Eleanor is still slightly suspicious of him and keeps her guard up. She fears the merchant's regular customers finding out who she is and turning her over to the authorities. She hopes that she will one day be able to speak openly about her interests and bond with others over her love of space. Eleanor does not yet appreciate her intelligence because she does not have access to enough books to satisfy her thirst for knowledge. The merchant does all he can but struggles to compete with other, more successful sellers.

Hopkins came to her town in 1645. Since Hopkins' arrival, Eleanor has become more cautious as many of the women she used to see on the street have disappeared.

Scene One

Eleanor is sitting on her bed reading The Assayer *by Galileo Galilei. She is humming a tune while flicking through the pages. Occasionally, she finds a particularly interesting part of the text and leans towards it with wide eyes. There are various piles of books about the Sciences under her bed. Wooden beams line the ceiling. Next to her bed is a small table with a candle placed on top, which can be seen from the street below through the harlequin-patterned window.*

Eleanor: The works of Galileo are fascinating; the depth of his work is incredible! I wonder how long he took to write this book? Maybe I will follow in his footsteps one day. Although, I could never hope to achieve even a fraction of his knowledge, especially in this less-than-fortunate situation. I would give anything to be rid of this superstitious Hopkins. He has convinced the entire town to keep an eye open for anyone with a suspicious-looking blemish or mark on their skin. And God forbid anyone owns a harmless cat – you might as well have sold your soul to the devil, according to Hopkins. Since he arrived, I have had to go to extreme lengths just to hide the fact that I like learning because he, and now the rest of the people in this town, believe it should be a death sentence for a woman.

Eleanor hears footsteps on the stairs. She throws the book under her bed and fumbles with her bed covers so that they cover her stash of reading materials.

Never Let Your Mistress Meet Your Dog

Ashlie Marrows

Yelling,
That's all I can hear,
Lots of yelling,
They've been like this for the past hour,
From hallway, to living room, to kitchen,
And it started when I brought a T-shirt downstairs that I found
    under his side of the bed.

She's crying,
He's pleading,
Like I plead for my squeaky toy back after I squeeze it
    one-too-many times.
I go up to comfort her and sit on her lap,
He shoves me away like a filthy rag no one wants to touch
    anymore,
Now she's angry.

There's a knock on the door,
An intruder?
I yap at the silhouette like my life depends on it,
He kicks me out of the way and scolds me as he comes to
    the door,
I run back to her,
She keeps me safe.

I watch as the silhouette rounds the corner,
Walking towards the intruder who so rudely is disrupting
    my home,

I gaze up and notice I don't need to bark as I usually do,
It's the nice blonde who comes round when she's out!
I curl up at her feet,
I see him hand back the shirt to her and the yelling resumes.

Family Reunion

Ashlie Marrows

Interviews by a Police Constable

The Grave Digger

'The day started like any other, with birds a'chirpin' and a pot
o'coffee brewing away, I begun me little mornin' chores. First, I
swept the kitchen floor, me little kitty is always trudgin' up mud
through the house, gettin' it right clarty.'

'Could we speed this along, sir?'

'Oh! Aye, of course officer. Well, I was walkin' me usual
route past the family who, every Sunday, visit their dear old
grandpa. It's very upsettin', he seemed a lovely bloke. Anyways!
There's gonna be a funeral in a day or two over on the west
side of the yard, so I trotted me way on over when I noticed
a young'un over on one of the newer additions to the place.
Only put 'er there a couple o'months ago. I thought she was
sleepin' and started t'yell at 'er and when she wasn't responding
I nudged 'er. She didn't utter a peep! I was yelling at 'er that
this wasn't the place to be for a kip and lo and behold,
there's a blow on the back of 'er head! Blood all o'er the lilies
on the grave. The dead's fella only left 'em there a few days
ago, actually.'

The Elderly Woman

'I witnessed a middle-aged chap bringing a spritely young missy
to the park. He was being rather rough-and-tumble with her,
shoving her towards the playing apparatus and yelling all

manner of ghastly things at the poor dear. Something about her being a good-for-nothing money-drainer, wishing he'd never had anything to do with her, grumbling about her constant asks for him to come play with her. She was brought half to tears! Even a couple of the parents seemed upset – it was not a pleasant atmosphere, not one bit. Just as I was about to educate this, this ruffian of a man on the importance of family and kindness towards the beings of our future, another man beat me to the punch! Quite literally, now I recall. See, they were effin' and blinding, and I went as pale as a poltergeist! I couldn't tell much about their faces – they were both hooded as most thugs are. Just when I thought it could not get any more indecent, one of the men pulled his fist back and landed it on the other's temple, knocking him clean out before taking the sweet child roughly by the arm, away from the scene, sternly meeting the gaze of every eye in there, as cold as a scolding mother could make it. That's the last I saw of her before I fled home.'

The Father

'So, it's midday on Saturday and my little girl comes barrelling into the sitting room. "Daddy, Daddy can I go to the park to meet a friend?" she screams at me.'

'I was hesitant, so I asked which friend, like any concerned person would. Now, when she said she had met her online, a red flag was raised, another swiftly following it when she told me she had no picture of them, she only knew her friend had 'pretty green eyes and blonde hair'. These red flags were accompanied with enough to supply an entire country when she then said how she trusts the person as she promised to bring gifts to the park when she next sees her. She pleaded with me for what felt like hours on end until the noise was akin to the harsh screeching of a car alarm. I caved because, at the end of the day, I would hate for my little girl to be upset with me, but I was smart with it. I decided to follow her. All the way to our local park. I wasn't born yesterday; I know how these things go. Trying to stay as inconspicuous as possible, I popped my hood up and walked closer to the edge of the park, looking at my phone as though it held all the secrets to the world. After I lost my wife recently, I just had to protect my little one. I wasn't prepared to lose another. You know how it is officer? I just couldn't.'

'I lost my husband and my two kids due to a rogue crook. Ran before I could apprehend him.'

'O-Oh. I'm so sorry about your loss sir, that must've been rough.'

'Uh huh.'

'So, erm, as I was saying, I was hanging about outside the park when I noticed a hooded man approach my darling, so naturally I went to confront him. No one lays a finger on my girl. The man was too close, so I grabbed his arm, and my daughter runs to get help from a nearby lady who my wife used to go to bingo with, so I knew she was safe. Or I thought she was. Next thing I know, a fist meets my face and I'm on the ground. Last thing I see before I pass out was that person dragging my little angel right to the graveyard. Oh God, what am I going to do...'

The Outsider

'Yes, it's true, I, er, I was at the park that day. Mother insisted I get some fresh air and yelled at me to comply. She can be truly annoying. I sneaked a hoodie in my bag so as not to worry, put it on as soon as she couldn't see me from the living room window. She always fusses, saying I've got no real friends, but I do! I definitely do! They're just not from around here; we play videogames all day together but apparently that's not good enough for her! Nothing is ever good enough for her. I digress. So, I was walking past the park on my way to my favourite shaded spot where I could sit on my phone when I suddenly heard this bellowing voice coming from a tall, also hooded man. It was freaky... like looking at a reflection on a rippling lake, slightly distorted but the message is still there. I was not about to let another child have a (REDACTED) of a parent like I had to have so, naturally, I stepped in to assist the young damsel in distress. Wait – can I swear on these recordings? No? Oh, you'd prefer me not to. No promises ha, ha! Not one for a joke? Right, a girl is dead. Almost forgot why I was here. He was being aggressive with her, calling her a (REDACTED) and the like. Oh (REDACTED)! Sorry, completely forgot about the rule thingy again. Anyway, I swooped in like the hero I am, yelling at him and as I pushed the girl out the way, he used my brief moment of weakness to knock me to the floor in a, quite frankly, cowardly move. Actually, as I remember it, I think I recognise the innocent thing. She was the daughter of this woman in Mum's book club; Lily, I think her name was. As my vision tunnelled in, I saw the child dragged into the neighbouring graveyard. Oh, my mother will be so disappointed in me when she finds out I didn't save her.'

Lindbergh Girl

Emily Freeman

Stilettos black, balancing a
Swaying gait with the pavements
Of Paris at the mercy of its knees

Slow-motion strides with aim;
Legs arrows, lethal and
Pointing towards some target
That one can only wish to

Look towards

A sheer skirt bunching
Into a blurring barricade,
Then releasing

Tension into windows;
Toned legs in view
Every two sharp seconds

A blazer cut out neat,
Sharp at the shoulders,
Nothing underneath;

The white filling is skin,
Folding creases: rare
Bones of the chest

Flexing with each
Swinging strike, intake
Of breath, inhalation

Of a cigarette, in then out,
The fumes left behind the
Wheels of something sexy.

Satin lips that blow
Kisses in the air, two pink
Ladies pursing

To nobody in particular;
A face wonders and
Blesses itself

Before the green eyes
That hold it like cement
Beneath feet.

Alt-16

Emily Freeman

Scene One

A small bedroom, dimly lit. The curtains are closed. There is a single bed, wardrobe, bedside table and various piles of clothes are strewn about the floor. Joy Division's album Closer *is playing in the background. There is a green strip-light that reveals a jet-black computer set-up in the corner of the room and a few posters of which the contents are not visible, besides one in the corner that depicts a beautiful, half-naked blonde woman, possibly from the 1930s. Alex is sitting at his computer, occasionally swirling around on his chair. He is dressed in plain black distressed jeans, a black hoodie that is zipped up, and black socks. A long, black jacket is hung on the back of his chair. He has dark brown, almost black hair that is more long than short. The paleness of his face is striking and his features are relatively sharp.*

Alex: This country is a mess. I'm sure you can agree. It's lost its greatness. We are nothing now. I think my friends think the same, but they're not as brave as me. Not brave enough to share their ideas. I don't go around shouting about my beliefs, of course; those self-proclaimed 'progressives' would never let me speak and, anyway, they wouldn't understand. Even before I consider opening my mouth, I can just hear the whining voice that'll be returned to me: *(he mimics)* 'racist', 'neo-Nazi', 'extremist'. The Internet is a better place for me. I'm part of groups where I'm not judged; I engage with like-minded people who give me new concepts to consider. No snowflakes, no lefties, no middle-class white girls to shut me up. A place where I belong. They think they're so enlightened, so brilliant and modern with their views. They think they're changing the world by sharing s****y slogans on their profiles, but there are those like me who know better. I've managed to gain quite a following too and, hopefully, someone will notice me. People need to realise this country needs an identity –

Alex's mother: (*offstage*) Alex!

Alex: (*rolling his eyes, ignoring her*) Not foreigners, feminists and gays. We need a new order, an aesthetic, a return to old social roles where everyone was happy. A strong military so that we feel protected, and a homogenous race so our British culture isn't threatened. Everything is all confused now, and nobody knows what's what. People call me a 'fascist', but I prefer 'identarian'.

Alex turns on the miniature architect's lamp on his desk, picks up a relatively thick book and reads from about a quarter of the way in. He takes notes every few seconds. He is disturbed by a buzz on his desktop. He turns over his phone.

Eighteen new followers today! See what I mean? People are understanding now. Eventually, I'll be noticed by people even bigger than me. I need to prove myself to them; maybe develop my own articles on nationalism or something like that. But I don't know how I could ever focus on my work when school is always getting in the way. What's important is the future. I don't want to be learning about other people; when I want to be the person people learn about. I do quite like history, though; it helps me realise my potential. And my teacher likes how I don't shy away from 'controversy'.

Alex's mother: Alex! Your tea is going cold! And you need to do your bloody washing from last week, you smelly little s**t. Now your sister's moved out, I can't do everything!

Alex ignores her, sighs and continues with his reading, occasionally stopping to write notes.

Get your useless arse down here now!

Alex throws the book down onto the desk and exits.

Red

Emily Freeman

Charlotte as a young child

Door slamming and Mummy
Screams, coming out from the room
Next to the room I play in.
Her face wet,
Like when I feel something is off in myself.
Black eyes
Like panda bear that I hug when
She can't hug me and
I have to go sleep because it's night-time and
The stars are out.
Daddy was at the opening near the black corry-door and
Closes it with the thing I can't reach and
The sound hurts me.
Mummy opens her mouth wide and scary shouting and
I am crawling on the sofa staring.
She is looking strange
Faces upside down on the floor
Fists in the air but not excited.
In the corner I was seeing Mummy and Daddy.
Both look upside down making loud words with
Shiny faces.
Red hands.
Cheater cheater cheater cheater cheater cheater cheater
I am pushed into bedtime but
It isn't dark

And panda is downstairs
And I haven't eaten Wednesday soup
And I haven't been read to.

Charlotte's father

She came home and told me she had
Cut herself on a knife again.
It was the cat last time, so
Vicious, that bastard, a mumble
As she walked away.
The rose bush – missing the thorns
Because the flowers were
So red.
Her arms were so red.
I can't leave her alone.
Not now. My conscience
Cannot permit another distraction
She has to be with me.

Charlotte's mother

I think every day, think – know – he doesn't want me. Just here
to pity me at daybreak and leave to go to bed in the afternoon.
The work parties. The work dos. He speaks to them all – Donna
the Blonde, Annie the Brunette, Carrie the Redhead – while I
am left with the kids in my state, rotting, watching TV after
I put them to bed. I would sit and sit and only the pain would
take all the sitting away. Without it, all I would think about is
how he would leave me, how he would leave the children and
how I mean nothing. I am nothing. The roses were so red

and he was away, so far away. So far. I had to. I made sure they didn't see, made sure they only saw the glinting dew petals flicker in the sun as I cleaned myself up inside.

'Look at how red they are, look.'

You see now. When he leaves I can't help myself. I am not selfish. He thinks I am selfish – but really, who is selfish when he is the one that yells, makes me cry? Makes the youngest cry, shoves her in bed each night it all happens. Shoves me in here, keeps me in here and tells me I can't leave – just in case. I know what the 'just in case' means. You're crazy. Crazy.

Charlotte as a young adult

Dear diary,

It happens all the time now, though I cannot work out what is in my head and what is not. I just remember red. Red faces. Red hands. Red fists. Red eyes. It was all red to me, the whole house. It got like that a few more times and I was shoved onto the sofa with Nellie. Nellie told me it wasn't my fault, though I still feel so guilty. Realistically, I know it isn't – my therapist told me it isn't. *Guilt is a useless feeling.* But I still feel as though it was. Maybe I was too much for her. I must have made it all worse for her when she had to take care of me, with what Dad did and everything. Nellie was old enough to understand, but I know she feels the same as me. Probably worse. When you're older it hits harder; when you're younger, well, there are just a lot of misconceptions to clear away. Lots of therapy sessions to attend, lots of soul-searching and all that s**t. Nellie knows it all, and she still won't tell me any of it, won't write about any of it and won't hear anything from Dad. I don't know if she blames him, and I don't know if I do either. I cannot blame because nothing is clear. I tried to remember what happened when I was very young today; but all I hear are phrases, and all I see is red and a black corridor. Roses in the garden. Look at the roses, don't look at me.

Love, Charlotte

The Life of a Fly

Emma Benton

A fly has few responsibilities.
No thoughts. No opinions. Just survival.
They live their short lives in blissful serenity,
with nothing harmful in sight except for being trapped behind
    clear glass.
Shards of grass the size of skyscrapers,
Raindrops the size of small planets,
People the size of giants.
To a fly, the world is something out of proportion, something
    strange and distorted.
To us, a fly is something minute and inconsequential,
    something which annoys us on a hot summer's day.
Untamed. Delicate. Fragile.
The life of a fly is something we could never imagine.

Troubled Youth

Emma Benton

Scene One

Set in a suburban American town, 2010. The scene opens with an empty bench in the middle of a field. An old woman slowly makes her way toward the bench, using her cane to balance herself. Her hair is black with grey streaks and she's wearing a plain T-shirt and a long skirt.

Maggie: *(Collapsing onto the bench, out of breath)* One could say I've had a good, long life. I have children, grandchildren and a husband. Back in my day, that was all that was expected of women. Oh, I remember my teenage years like it was yesterday. Skipping school, doing drugs, protesting women's rights and beating up racists – the usual. Each time the phone rings or I get a knock on my door, I think it's the police finally catching up with me. My heart skips a beat. Then I realise – we were wearing masks, we were anonymous. Not a single day goes by where I don't think and laugh about all the dodgy situations we put ourselves in and all the times we nearly got caught. But we were never caught. We were too careful. The day they figure out it was us is the day pigs fly.

She laughs and pulls herself up from the bench. She takes her phone from her purse and we hear her making a call as she walks away.

Scene Two

Maggie enters her best friend's house, taking her shoes off and sitting down on the living room sofa.

Trisha: Make yourself comfortable.

Trisha is the same age as Maggie. She is wearing her gym clothes, mainly Nike products. She started exercising and changing her life in her early 40s. They settle in for their usual Friday night with a bottle of wine and a tub of 'Ben & Jerry's' chocolate chip ice-cream.

Maggie: What the bloody hell are you wearing?

Trisha: My gym clothes – you know how I like to exercise and keep my eyes on the prize!

They both laugh.

            I wish we could go back and relive every moment of our lives. We didn't make the most of it when we were that young and, look at us now, sat around wasting our time watching TV!

Maggie: Do you ever regret it?

Trisha: What?

Maggie: What do you think? Robbing that last bank, becoming outlaws, being on the FBI's most-wanted list. The thing that caused us to never have a moment of happiness without looking over our shoulders.

The Life of a Plant

Kia Williams

Plants live a life so unique, so still and silent,
making us question their existence.
How can these strange things really have a life?
Life is oh so different for these little plants.

What happens when we poke them?
Do they hurt? Do they cry?
These little plants, delicate and fragile,
they are living like me and you.

Life is oh so different, but so similar too.
They grow so fast and then they die.
They don't talk, they can't communicate.
But who knows, maybe this is a good thing after all?

Tattooed on Our Minds

Kia Williams

Statement by Tom's Best Friend, Ben

It was a normal Friday evening; I remember the day so clearly. The sun was slowly descending as the moon rose high to take its place in the evening sky. Tom and I had finished playing our game of football, something we did most Fridays after school. As we walked home, the streetlights towered over us as if they were protecting us from something evil. When we reached the end of the street, we parted company with clenched fists – we always gave a fist-bump, it was our thing. We smiled at each other. The lights above reflected into Tom's glassy blue eyes. I wish I could re-live that moment. It replays over and over, on repeat, in my head. It was silent on my way home. I thought about what we had planned for the following week. We agreed that, on Monday after school, we would go to the big football field again to practise for our team game. One day, we said, we would go into town for some lunch.

I reached home and went upstairs to my bedroom. After a few hours, I fell asleep; but not for long because my phone rang – Tom's mum, Louise. It was unusual, she barely ever called. 'Where was Tom?'

A rush of adrenaline flooded my body. Suddenly, I was wide awake. So many emotions, so many questions filled my head. Where was my best friend?

Statement by Tom's Sister, Sofia

As soon as Tom left for football practice, I jumped into my cosy pyjamas and began counting down the hours until we could start our brother and sister film evening. I waited as patiently as I could. After finishing the dinner Dad made us, I set out the living room. He had told me on the way home from school that we could watch a film together and I could choose the film. I was so excited. I brought my best blankets down from my bedroom and laid them neatly onto the big sofa. I had my pillows too and I was pushing the feathers, that were trying to escape, back into place. I brushed my hand over the soft blanket, admiring its sparkles. In a plastic bowl were the snacks we had picked out the night before: sweet-smelling popcorn, sour red sweets, delicately-wrapped milk chocolate and some crisps. After what seemed like a lifetime, the clock struck 7 p.m. Tom would be back anytime soon. I quickly moved to the window, closing the old, cream-coloured blinds protecting us from the outside. I squinted into the darkness. Tom didn't come home on time. It was getting late. Mum and Dad told me to go to bed; we could re-arrange the film night. I didn't argue but I fled upstairs, the tears blurring my vision. Where was my big brother?

Statement by Tom's dad, George

I pulled up on the drive, parked the car and double-checked it was locked. As I turned, my beloved son Tom was there grinning at me. I knew where he was going: him and Ben always looked forward to their weekly football. I told him to be careful and make sure he was back in time for 7 p.m. Inside, I set to cooking the dinner. My wife, Louise, had laid the table, waiting for the food to arrive. The pans were heating on roaring blue flames and the smell of spices filled the house. I left Tom's portion covered up for him to have later. It was his favourite meal. After dinner, me and Louise scrolled through our phones while Sofia set the sofa for their movie night. Tom's food was going cold; he was nowhere to be seen. He'd told me he'd be careful and come home on time. Where was my son? Why wasn't he home?

Statement by Tom's mum, Louise

When Sofia went to bed, me and George sat together, our hands interlinked. Every so often my eyes turned to the clock, which continued to tick. Still no sign of Tom. I picked up my phone, my palms were sweating, and called him again. Straight to voicemail. I typed another message and clicked 'send'. He should have received these calls and messages, unless his phone had died. I called Ben, Tom's best friend. The last time he saw Tom was when they'd finished football. He asked if he could help in any way? He was scared, I knew he was. Everyone was. My heart pounded in my chest and it pulsed through my ears. Pacing around the kitchen, my hands shaking, I decided to call the police. Where was my son?

Tom

As I was walking along, I could hear a sound other than my own footsteps. I gripped my football in my hands. When I picked my sister up from school, I promised her we could watch a film and have some snacks later. I glanced at my wristwatch – 6.45 p.m. I should be home on time. Perfect. Tonight's game had been amazing. We were practising lots of different techniques and worked a lot on our aim. It was a lovely night; the moon was starting to shine and the sky was turning grey. There wasn't a person in sight. My stomach was grumbling, muttering to me it was hungry. I kicked pebbles out of the way, pretending I was back on the football field, my favourite place. I was looking forward to the evening ahead. I was caught by surprise when the footsteps grew louder and quicker. I glanced around but didn't really think anything of it. My football fell to the ground, and I reached to get it as it tumbled along the road. Then something was pulling me towards the trees. I saw my watch – 7 p.m., as I tried to push my way out of the bushes. Everything went into slow-motion. My life flashed before my eyes and closed. Darkness.

Celestial Entities

Kiki Shodimu

Humongous they were.
Intimidating beings with crude humour,
Something beyond the cerebrum's capacity.
They exuded arrogance from their very pores,
contaminating the polluted air around them;
marched around Mother Nature's territory,
constricting her from flourishing,
as though they held and nurtured it for nine months.
Humongous they were.

Mother Nature

Kiki Shodimu

With one word, I'm told I'm not burning from within, as if
the coal burning up my ribcage isn't proof enough. As if the
unpredictable mood swings that tremble the Earth's very core
isn't proof enough. As if my tears aren't barricaded with the
plastic that fills them up, till the chokehold reaches its limit.
You see, my days are numbered, gone are the fragments of my
childhood. Gone is the innocent naivety that once filled the
Earth with rich warmth. I'm tired, I have been for a while now.

A Dictatorship

Laura Richardson

Time
   is like a heartbeat;
it beats
      without thought –
something
that cannot be caught.
A clock
      on the wall
dictating
when,
where,
who
I am.
It decides
everything
and no one begins to
realise
that time
is like a
disease. An
      infestation.
A paralysing
thought –
something
that cannot
be bought.
They go through life
not caring

unaware
that their
      time
is diminishing,
my time
      is
      diminishing.
We all want
more
time
      but time
does not
last forever.

From the Third Galaxy to the Left

Laura Richardson

Butterflies,
not like the ones we see in summer
that flutter
in the breeze. I mean
the ones that weaken my knees.
The ones
that appear just before the first day of school,
the time you are waiting
after you broke a rule.
The ones that appear
before you have your first kiss
or that appear when
you meet someone you don't want to miss.
The feeling
of when the butterflies leave
and are replaced with joy or fear,
when that someone
whispers in your ear.
The sound of laughter,
an indescribable muffle
of sounds and breaths
that send people into a kerfuffle.
The build-up of trust and
love
and all the feelings above,
what is beyond the atmosphere
and what we feel down here.
No two people are the same

and yet we all share the blame
of hate
and anguish
and we still struggle to establish
that we are all equal,
no matter what.

Calcium

Lauren Betts

Earth's bones. Beautiful pool of silence,
back again to add to the stolen artefacts.
A place for those to open mouths and
gaze through glass. The emotions that
once were raw, the human swish against
bodies in yaw cease to stay forever in a
gaze just a disintegration maze. Each grain
of soil, a decoration perhaps, falling around
the body like a time relapse – such structure
stays forever, in memory, on paper, by
days in the fall of a feather. Nightfall comes
and it becomes one. Under is over. Those
that are lost are no longer gone insightful,
pastimes sending ripples of silent riptides.
Perhaps we are all underground – there is
no right way around just the sounds of
falling ashes to the ground. Speckled
raindrops dripping – we are already there.
Treacherous parts like a winter's play park.
Still. Smiles cracked in a bowl of sores, bleeding
lips pouring in and out of souls until the bark
is lit and we see the mould and become no
longer what we are told.

Our Shared Thorns

Lauren Betts

It's intolerable to lie under the tree,
the shadow hooded
over as a cage sewn
into the Earth as a
natural barrier. It
forces my lenses to
watch the
mundanity repeat
itself. Each rib
divulges into a deep
cacophony casket,
wrecking wind of
gust and might,
tearing into another
side. Layers pulled
apart, dripping
deep into heated
soil that remains
stained, only
growing thicker in
plight. I will do the
same later. My
teeth ring with pain
yet fill the spasm in
my stomach.
Pulsating when the
print I own patterns
the paint of death.

Pretty. Swaying
when I drag it back
to the hole I
tainted. When the
horde comes,
sinking through into
the depths, I will
disappear. Thorns
sunk into the skull
to make my body
dear. Bloody clots
oxygenating
another, decorated
around the softness
of mouth – a reward
reaped well.
Enough to feed the
next decade of
decay. My relations
will not mourn,
blew the slicing
winds adorned.

Climate Change

Michael March

With one breath, you tell me my voice, my opinions are
    listened to, valid, understood,
But when the same voice tries to bring about even the smallest
    change, it's angry, childish and 'not backed up'.
You see the news, have sympathy, learn that disasters are a
    result of human mistakes,
But when given the opportunity to stop it, you have no
    empathy and you will not partake.
What's the statistic? In eleven years, the damage is irreversible.
You know, but act like the Earth is something that is
    reimbursable.
When I talk about this, you roll your eyes, let the responsibility
    fall onto me and my generation,
When you are the ones with the power, the vote, but where is
    your participation?

Not the Same

Michael March

The sun's still bright, bright enough to make me squint, but it's paler, like the saturation is turned down, the sky is still blue, but the sort of blue that you would get if the clouds had swirled in, dull,

The clouds still roll across the horizon, but they no longer depict the castles, faces, dragons they used to – they just block out the sun, making everything a little more grey,

The clock still ticks and the pendulum that my head used to subconsciously follow, still rocks, but the sound no longer entices me to mimic it or dance in a robot-like way,

The grass hills are still there, yet they don't seem to scintillate the yellow light of summer or invite me to roll down them, they just provide a longer journey home,

The floor still wears the same carpet, yet it no longer turns to lava making everyone cling to the sofa or throw pillows down as stepping-stones, it simply collects dust, another thing to clean,

The sticks still reside on the forest floor, yet they no longer resemble knights' swords, Gandalf's staff, witches' wands, they're just obstacles on the path,

The books still hold the same adventures, but they don't seem to transport me to other worlds in the same way the used to,

It's not the same.

A Vampire's Lament

Rory-Jae North

My heart is too stubborn to beat,
My blood rests halted in my vessel.
It's stagnant.
Stale air still pocketed in my inflated lungs,
Leaving my sternum to ache with the cold.

This suit of porcelain,
Icy, pale, gaunt.
This blue-lipped grin,
Ivory-filled and stained.
Glazed eyes filter darkness
To hide the red mass of thought curling behind them.

Call me a monster, call me damned.
See the limits of the cards in my hand
And forgive me my inherent monstrosities.
The devil is so cruel a dealer.

My dear, I can never warm you.
But will me to open the cage of my ribs
And I'll help you crawl in,
Nestle against the chilled marble of my heart.
Warm me from the inside.

Let me plait your hair,
Clash our teeth,
Cool your feverish skin.
Force me to spit your blood,
It's iron taste on my back teeth too sweet to swallow.

Though I love you I can't make you last.
I will consume you,
Slowly, and from afar,
Driven by an insatiable appetite.
I promise you won't feel my canines in your heart,
Until you awake in the darkness with a halted system,
Made thick with my sweet toxin,
My thin fingers wrapped around your hand.

Together Apart

Sam King

These walls seize me
A prison with no key
The world around me darkened
And no one could see

Everyday was the same
No difference between Monday Tuesday
Wednesday Thursday alike
That was until I got your call

We spoke about our day
And how we both wished we could escape
We laughed and we cried
And wished to be face to face

And I felt less alone
I knew you were there
A window opened
I gained a smile

The world now seemed brighter
A flame flickered around me
And I'm more okay within these walls
With you by my side

BIOGRAPHIES

ABIGAIL HORNE: In the words of Elon Musk, 'Take risks now and do something bold, you won't regret it.' So put your pen to paper and have fun.

ALISHA KNOWLES: I really enjoy listening to a wide variety of music, from musicals to indie pop. I also like learning my favourite songs on my guitar. I spend a lot of my time at concerts and reading books by Peter James. I spend a lot of my time watching streamers on Twitch, mainly 'Foolish Gamers'.

ANNIE LEWIS: I'm fluent in three languages: English, French and Swankalishious.

ASHLIE MARROWS: Physically I'm fine, emotionally I'm bruised.

EMILY FREEMAN: Emily is an old soul. Emily's favourite colour is grey, but she insists she isn't necessarily boring. Emily has been described as being more similar to a middle-aged individual than a girl of seven and ten years. Emily drinks black coffee without the sugar. Emily reads a newspaper weekly. Emily is rather pretentious. Emily despises digital clocks. Emily listens to records every Friday evening. Emily loves Joy Division and often wishes she could live in black and white, or some sepia tone. Emily is very 'glass half-empty'. Emily likes reading – a lot. Emily still maintains that *Romeo and Juliet* is not an over-rated tragedy. Emily has an obsession with Sylvia Plath – it is concerning. Emily idolises sad writers a little too much. Emily wants to be a poet.

EMMA BENTON: 'Hi this is Emma, I can't come to the phone right now. Don't leave a voicemail, a text or an email. Leave me alone.'

KIA WILLIAMS: When I write, all my thoughts and feelings switch from my head to the paper lying before me. Writing allows your imagination to run completely free.

KIKI SHODIMU: Hey dude, my name's Kiki, which you probably know from that irritating Drake song, 'Worst Behaviour', if I'm being honest; but thanks for the screen time. Bestie xoxo.

LAURA RICHARDSON: Poetry: a cluster of words that sing the melody of those who wish to write it. They form and transmit our lives into something that doesn't fit the societal norms. People laugh and people cry; one of whom, is me. I use the words to find a clue of where I stand in society. Now take a breath, look outside, and listen to the words of the cow: moo.

LAUREN BETTS: Behind each cylindrical mass is a story. I decided to peel off my mask in fury. My writing is a segment of me, a tiny dot that you'll see. Let it be as much of me, as of you. I pulled apart my limbs and found a message inside. A daily manifesto perhaps. It said something to me. Ink reaching page is our only hope for now. No. Forever.

MICHAEL MARCH: A wise poet once said: 'Just keep breathing and breathing and breathing…'

RORY-JAE NORTH (they/them): Hello, I'm Rory, I love classic literature and my favourite book is *Carmilla*. Writing is a fun escape for me and writing poetry has been an interesting change from what

I usually do. I hope to be a publisher one day and work with other writers and editors and really connect with others' work and eventually better my own!

SAM KING: Je ne parle pas français.

Acknowledgements

Melanie Curtis at Avon DataSet for her overwhelming support for First Story and for giving her time in typesetting this anthology.

Sally Beets for copy-editing and Sophie Blacksell Jones for proof-reading this anthology.

The Man Trout for illustrating the cover of this anthology.

Foysal Ali at Aquatint for printing this anthology at a discounted rate.

The Dulverton Trust for supporting First Story in this school.

HRH The Duchess of Cornwall, Patron of First Story.

The Founders of First Story:
Katie Waldegrave and William Fiennes.

The Trustees of First Story:
Ed Baden-Powell (chair), Aziz Bawany, Aslan Byrne, Sophie Harrison, Sue Horner, Sarah Marshall, Bobby Nayyar, Jamie Waldegrave and Ella White.

Thanks to our funders:
Amazon Literary Partnership, the Artists' Copyright and Licensing Society, Arts Council England, BBC Children in Need, Fiona Byrd, Beth & Michele Colocci, The Blue Thread, Didymus, the Dulverton Trust, the Garfield Weston Foundation, the Goldsmith's Company Charity, Granta Trust, Jane & Peter Aitken, John R Murray Charitable Trust, Letters Live, Man Charitable Trust, The Mayor's Young Londoners Fund, the Mercers' Company Charity, the Network for Social Change, the Paul Hamlyn Foundation, the Stonegarth Fund, Tim Bevan & Amy Gadney, the Unwin Charitable Trust, the Walcot Foundation, the Whitaker Charitable Trust, the Friends of First Story and our regular supporters, individual donors and those who choose to remain anonymous.

Pro bono supporters and delivery partners including:
Authorfy, BBC Teach, British Library, Cambridge University, Centre for Literacy in Primary Education, Driver Youth Trust, English and Media Centre, Forward Arts Foundation, Greenwich University, Hachette, National Literacy Trust, Penguin Random House and Walker Books.

Most importantly we would like to thank the students, teachers and writers who have worked so hard to make First Story a success this year, as well as the many individuals and organisations (including those who we may have omitted to name) who have given their generous time, support and advice.